My family is going camping on a campsite.

First we will put up our tent in a field.

Then we will cook some food.

At bedtime we will get inside the tent
and sleep.

1

Here we are in the campsite.

We are in a big field.

Here is the tent.

We help Dad.

We can eat here.

We can play here.

We are in the tent.